This book belongs to:

_____

MESSAGE TO PARENTS

This book is perfect for parents and children to read aloud together. First read the story to your child. When you read the story a second time, run your finger under each line, stopping at each picture for your child to "read." Help your child to figure out the picture. If your child makes a mistake, be encouraging as you say the right word. Point out the pictures and words that are printed in the margin of each page. Soon your child will recognize the picture symbols and be "reading" aloud with you.

ISBN: 1-56288-222-8   Library of Congress Catalog Card Number: 91-77734
Printed in the U.S.A.   0 9 8 7 6 5 4 3

The Story of Jonah

A Read Along With Me® Book

Retold by **Laurence Schorsch**
Illustrated by **Ying-Hwa Hu**

Checkerboard Press
New York

city

people

Jonah

Many, many years ago the 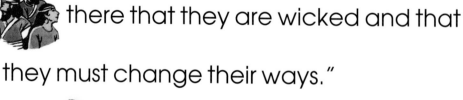 of Nineveh was full of wicked . One day God spoke to his prophet and said, "Go to the of Nineveh. Tell the there that they are wicked and that they must change their ways."

did not want to go to Nineveh.

So 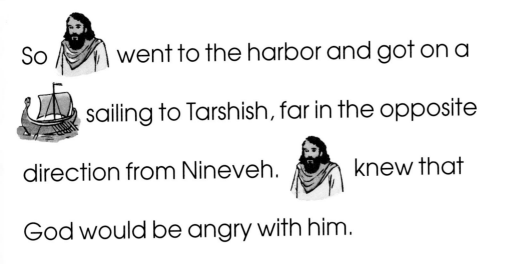 went to the harbor and got on a sailing to Tarshish, far in the opposite direction from Nineveh. knew that God would be angry with him.

And God was angry. When he saw that was on the , he sent a strong that made the very rough. The  was tossed up and down on the waves. The were afraid. They feared that the would sink and that they would all drown.

"Throw everything on the into the !" shouted one of the . "If we lighten the load, the will not sink!"

ship

wind

sea

sailors

sailors

wind

sea

Jonah

"Let us pray to our gods for help!"

shouted another. The  prayed as

loudly as they could to their gods. But the

grew fiercer and the became

rougher.

All the while slept in his cabin.

When the found sleeping, they

were very angry. They woke up and

asked him, "How can you sleep when our

is sinking? Who are you? Where do you come from?"

"I am a Hebrew," answered. "And though I fear God, I have disobeyed him. God is angry with me."

"What does your God want? What can we do to lessen his anger?" asked the . "Hebrew, we beg you, pray to your God and ask him to stop the ."

ship

sea

sea

Jonah

wind

ship

sailors

"Throw me into the 🌊!" said 👤.
"Then the 🌬 will cease and the 🌊
will become calm."

"If we do that, you will drown. Let us
try to row our 🚢 to the safety of the
shore," said the 👥. But the 🌊 was
too rough, and the fierce 🌬 kept
blowing the 🚢 farther from the shore.

At last the 👥 said, "We must throw
👤 into the 🌊. It is the only way to
save ourselves and our 🚢."

So the unhappy 👥 threw Jonah
overboard. Then the 👥 prayed to
God, "Do not be angry with us for throwing

 into the . For told us that

he disobeyed you, and therefore you

have sent this terrible storm."

wind

sea

sailors

Jonah

All at once the  stopped blowing and the became calm. The gave prayers of thanks to God.

Meanwhile  sank to the bottom of the and was swallowed by a great

. sat inside the belly of the

for three days and three nights. All that

time prayed. God heard his prayers

and forgave him. God told the to

carry  to shore and set him free.

whale

Jonah

people

city

man

woman

child

Then God said to 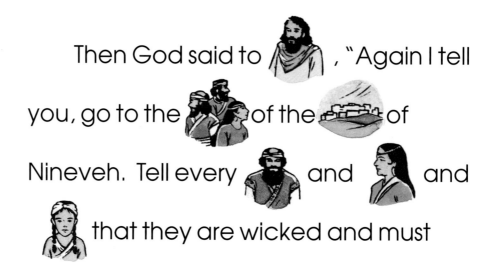, "Again I tell you, go to the of the of Nineveh. Tell every and and that they are wicked and must change their ways."

This time  did as God told him.

He went to the 🏙 of Nineveh and said

to the 👥, "In forty days God will

destroy your 🏙."

The 👥 of Nineveh were afraid

when they heard the words of 🧔. They

cried in fear, "We must fast to show our

obedience to God!" And from the richest

to the poorest, the 👥 fasted.

Jonah

king

man

woman

child

animals

people

It was not long before 's words reached the of Nineveh. The commanded that not only should every  , and fast but that all of the  must fast as well.

"We are indeed wicked," the told the . "If we change our ways,

God may forgive us and spare our ."

Then the  took off his royal robes and

sat in ashes. And the cattle did not graze

and the chickens did not peck.

city

man

woman

child

city

animals

people

Jonah

And God saw that every  and and in the of Nineveh was sorry, and so were all the . He saw that they had changed their ways. So God forgave the of Nineveh and did not destroy the .

But became angry. He said to God, "You made me come all the way to Nineveh to warn the that their would be destroyed. But because you are a merciful God, you forgave the . And the has not been destroyed. You have made me suffer for nothing!"

Then went outside of the

and made himself a small  and sat in

it. He waited to see what would happen

to the .

That night God made a large

grow by the side of the  to give

shade. And  liked sitting in the shade

of the .

hut

tree

tree

wind

Jonah

city

But the next night God made a worm that ate the , and the  died. Then God sent a hot and made the sun beat down on . Now  became even angrier.

"Why did you make me come to this wicked ?" he asked God. "Again you have made me suffer!"

But God said to 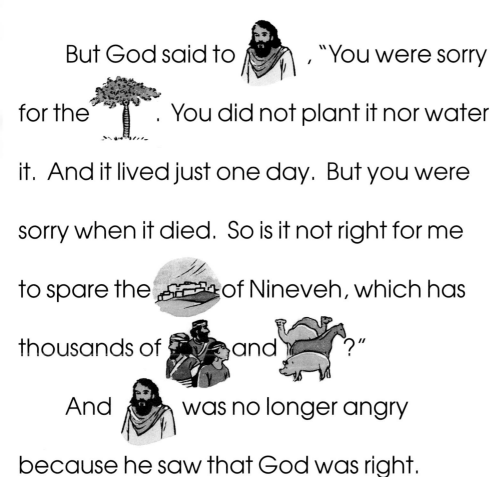, "You were sorry for the 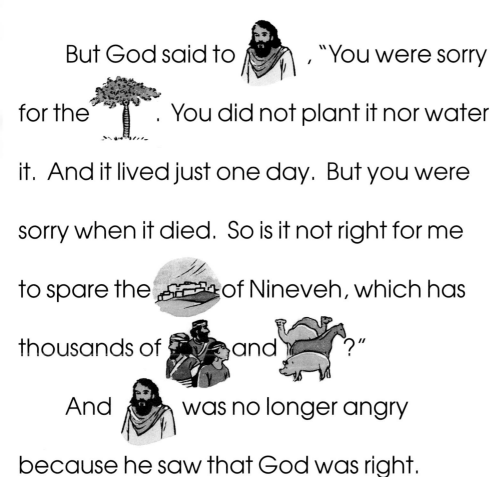. You did not plant it nor water it. And it lived just one day. But you were sorry when it died. So is it not right for me to spare the 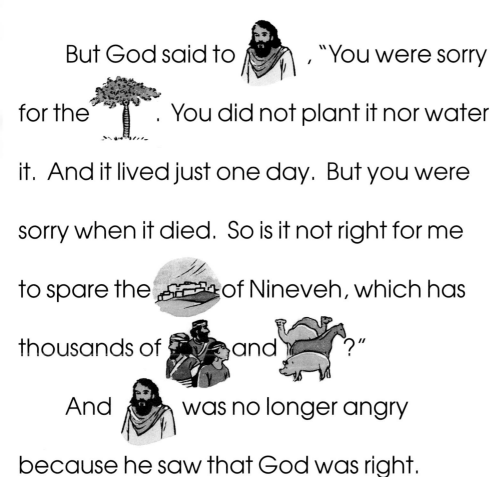 of Nineveh, which has thousands of 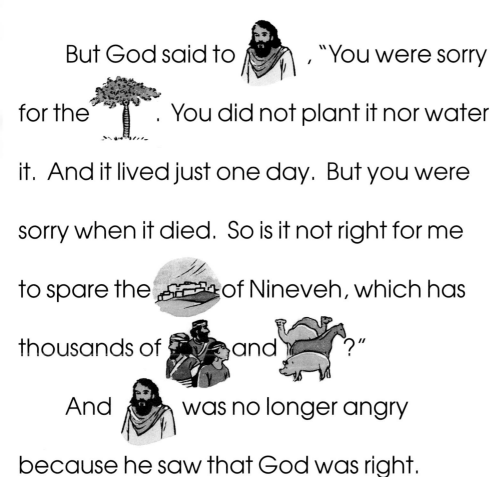 and 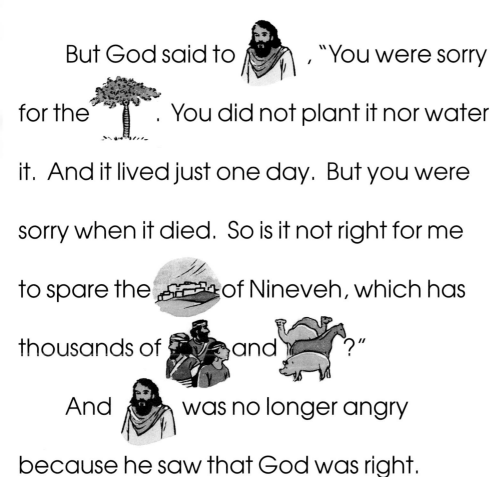?"

And 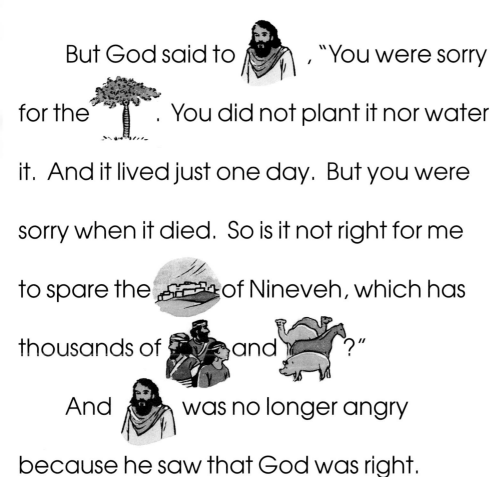 was no longer angry because he saw that God was right.

people

animals

Books I have read:

☐ David and Goliath

☐ Noah's Ark

☐ The Story of Jonah

☐ The Story of Joseph

The **Read Along With Me**® series is a collection of stories from the Bible, classic fairy tales and fables, and modern stories for parents and children to enjoy together.

How High?

Sasha and Cody want to see who can swing higher. Find the hidden objects in this scene. Place a sticker on each one.

Art by Karen Stormer Brooks

1

Our Backyard

Everyone in the family has something to do on a summer Saturday afternoo

Beach Builders

Jake has found another seashell to decorate the sandcastle he and Sherry built.

Art by Susan T. Hall

Skating Pond

At last, the ice is thick enough for everyone to skate.

Art by Charles Jordan

At the Playground

These friends are having lots of fun. What do y̶ the playground?

Art by Gary Mohrman

Art by R. Michael Palan

Floating Fun

These friends have a handy way to blow bubbles.

Art by Viki Woodworth

Trail Ride

For Kayla, riding a horse is the best part of her family's vacation.

Art by Ellen Appleby

Answers

How High? PAGE 1

Our Backyard PAGES 2–3

Six Years Old PAGE 4

Beach Builders PAGE 5

Skating Pond PAGES 6–7